LOVE
IS WHAT MATTERS MOST

Written by Carissa Nava

Story inspired by Trish Liberatore

Copyright©2020 Carissa Nava

Illustrations by Abida Eman

ISBN: 978-0-578-73643-3 (paperback)

To my children, Chloe and Colton.
Thank you for always inspiring me.
I love you more than the world.

Once upon a time there were four best friends,
They played together at school and on the weekends.

There were three little girls and one little boy.
Their names were Chloe, Jules, Colton and
last but not least, Joy.

They liked to play on the swings and would have
fun all day in the park.
And when it was time to go home they'd hear, "c'mon it's
time to leave" their mommies and daddies would remark.

Chloe had a mommy and a daddy who loved her a lot.
But not any more than Joys two daddy's that she's got.
And Jules had two mommies who loved her more than
the world which was known.
But just the same as Colton's mommy,
who did her mommy duties alone.

That night when they got home, Jules mommies
went to say goodnight to Jules in bed.
"Why don't I have a daddy? And why
does Joy get two?" she said.

Jules mommies both looked at each other and one of them said, "The answer is simple if you have this part: There are lots of different families, but having love in a family is what matters most and that comes from the heart."

A few days later, Joy had some questions for her daddies too.
"Why do some of my friends have mommies
and why for daddies do I have two?"

"That's a good question," one daddy said.
"The answer is simple as long as you have this part:
Love is what matters most and that comes from the heart."

And then came Colton, with a bunch of questions for his mom one night.
"Why do I only have one parent? Isn't having two what's right?"

"That's not true," said Colton's mommy. "The answer is simple as long as you have this part: Love is what matters most and that comes from the heart."

The very next day, the kids were playing
in the park together as they do.
They were on the swings, the
seesaw and the slide too.

Jules stopped for a moment and saw a little
girl standing alone with her teddy bear.
The little girl looked sad. Jules tried not to stare.

Colton Chloe and Joy continued to play.
But Jules left her swing and walked over that way.
Jules went over to the bench and said "Hi,
I'm Jules. What's your name?"
"I'm Maeve," the little girl said.
"I'm so glad you said hi and came."

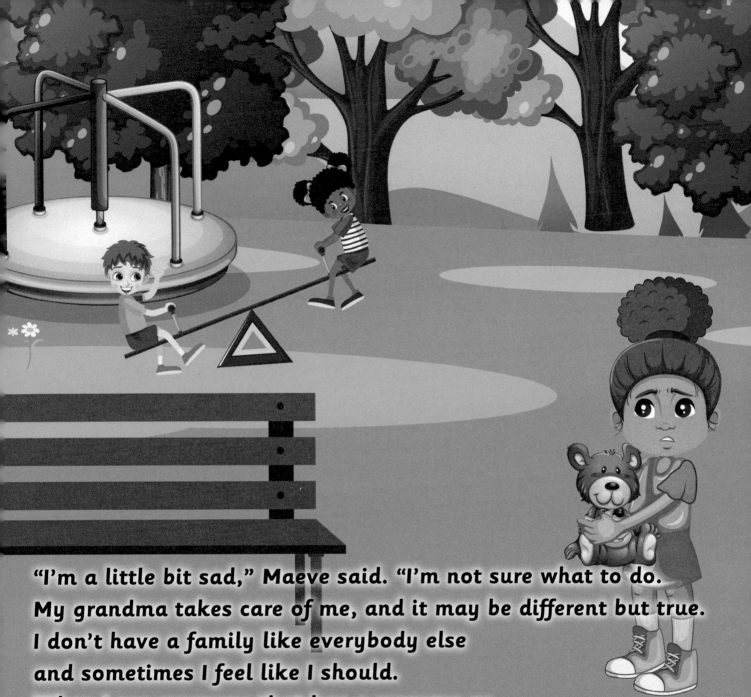

"I'm a little bit sad," Maeve said. "I'm not sure what to do.
My grandma takes care of me, and it may be different but true.
I don't have a family like everybody else
and sometimes I feel like I should.
When I see everyone that has a mommy or
daddy, it doesn't make me feel good."

"I'm sorry," said Jules. "But there's one thing
you should know from the start.
Love is what matters most and that comes from the heart."
"Families come in all shapes and sizes.
That's what my mommies say.
Love is all you need in a family. And I'm
sure you feel that every day."

Maeve knew Jules was right. She had a big smile on her face.
Being different is great and something we should all embrace.

From that day on, there were 5 best friends who played on the playground.

They all had different families with one thing in common...love.
And that's what makes the world go 'round!

Made in the USA
Monee, IL
25 September 2020